The One Day Creative Retreat Activity Book uses the ancient Monastic Hours to divide the day into different activities.

Pages from:

None
The ninth monastic hour.

None or the Ninth Hour is said around 3 p.m. Its name comes from Latin and refers to the ninth hour of the day after dawn.

The Lord your God is in your midst, a mighty one who will save; He will rejoice over you with gladness; He will quiet you by His love; He will exult over you with loud singing. Zephaniah 3:17 (ESV)

Write a short invitation prayer to use when you want to welcome God into a situation or use the prayer below.

Thank you for this moment,
May it be sacred,
O God,
make it Yours,

Thank you for this life,
May I be ready,
O God,
make me Yours,

Thank you for this voice,
May it be prayer,
O God,
make it Yours.

A good starting point for writing a prayer is the ACTS acrostic...

Adoration - love God

Confession - sorry God

Thanksgiving - thank God

Supplication - ask God

Forgiveness

Pages from:

Then Jesus said,
"Father, forgive them, for they do not know what they do."
Luke 23:34

Have you ever been stopped in your tracks by what a friend of mine used to call 'cringes'? Flashback memories of things you wish you hadn't done or said or that you wish you had done differently? If memories continue to 'haunt' you then the situations may not have ever been resolved.

Forgiveness isn't easy, I suspect that our human nature desires more to gain revenge than to forgive, forgiveness isn't something we can do in our own strength.

Follow one of the knots on the next page with your finger and pause where it crosses. When you pause think about the cringes that remain, the mistakes that haunt us when we're tired and low, the things we thought we had let go of but somehow they continue to stifle us.

Say out loud,
"With God's help I release these memories and I forgive myself and [n]."

Follow the other knot with your finger and pause where it crosses. When you pause think about someone who has hurt you in some way.

Say out loud,
"With God's help I forgive [n] and I ask for Your healing."

[n] = name of person

The Advent Creative Retreat Activity Book follows the story of The Other Wise Man and uses that and the liturgical colours of the season to inspire the activities.

Pages from:

Reasons to be Joyful

In the late seventies a popular song listed 'Reasons to be Cheerful' it had a catchy tune and taught a simple lesson in counting your blessings.

Write a list of ten things that make you feel joyful today...

1
2
3
4
5
6
7
8
9
10

Every day from today write down three things, one thing that makes you joyful, one thing that you are thankful for and one thing that you feel helpless about.

Tell God about them.

It may help to have three pebbles and a small cross, as you think of the things place them at the foot of the cross.

Thanks

Help

Love

What is Love?

Follow the spiral to the centre with your finger and think about what love means to you personally then from the centre say the words from Corinthians as you return to the start.

For God so loved the world, that He gave his only begotten Son, that whosoever believeth in Him should not perish, but have everlasting life.

LOVE ALWAYS PROTECTS. LOVE ALWAYS TRUSTS. LOVE ALWAYS HOPES. LOVE ALWAYS PERSEVERES. LOVE IS NOT EASILY ANGERED. LOVE KEEPS NO RECORD OF WRONGS. LOVE DOES NOT DELIGHT IN EVIL. LOVE REJOICES WITH THE TRUTH. LOVE IS NOT PROUD. LOVE DOES NOT DISHONOUR OTHERS. LOVE IS NOT SELF-SEEKING. LOVE DOES NOT ENVY. LOVE DOES NOT BOAST. LOVE IS KIND. LOVE IS PATIENT.

Jesus teach me how to love, how to live in Your presence.
Jesus teach me how to live, how to pray in Your will.
Jesus teach me how to pray, how to rest in Your embrace.
Jesus teach me how to rest, how to be in Your world.
Jesus teach me how to be, how to love in Your way.

The Holiday Creative Retreat Activity Book is loosely divided into times of the day but is easy to dip into.

Elevensies

[Martha] had a sister called Mary, who sat at the Lord's feet listening to what He said.
Luke 10:39

Get yourself a hot drink and find somewhere quiet to sit.

Jesus has many things to say to us today but in the busy-ness of life it can be difficult to just stop and listen, most of us are like Martha, over-concerned about keeping all our little juggling balls in the air because we know that if we let them fall it will be even harder to perform later. The story of Mary and Martha isn't suggesting that we drop all our responsibilities, it's about being willing to drop them when God wants us to, it's about being willing to have God change our priorities and focus.

He who is a child of God listens to God's words.
John 8:47

Now, for the next half hour or so try to be a deliberate Mary. Imagine yourself sitting with Jesus. What is He saying to you? What do you most want, or need, to hear today?

Prayer

Jesus I sit at Your feet,
Open my heart to Your presence,
Open my ears to Your words,
Open my mind to the wonder of You.

Sometimes it can be easier to listen to God and to pray if you have something to occupy your hands and distract your mind away from everyday concerns.

Opposite is a technique for using your hands to help your mind to focus.

With a finger from your other hand follow the pattern,
it doesn't matter where you start. Pray at each point
of the 'knot' and where the lines intersect over your palm.
You could pray something like this:

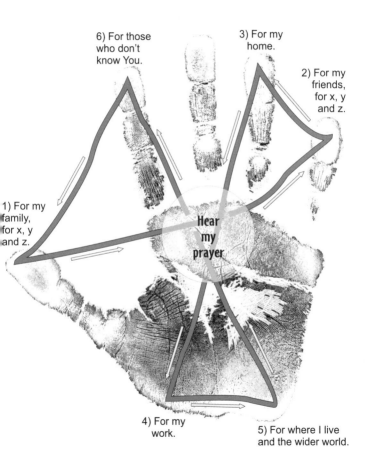

6) For those who don't know You.

3) For my home.

2) For my friends, for x, y and z.

1) For my family, for x, y and z.

Hear my prayer

4) For my work.

5) For where I live and the wider world.

BLESSED ARE THE PEACEMAKERS,

FOR THEY WILL BE CALLED THE CHILDREN OF GOD.

Page from:

Watch and Pray

Have you seen our other activity books?

The multicoloured range of colouring books range in size from A4 to A6 and are titled Multicoloured Prayers (A4), Meditations (A5), Devotions (A5), Blessings (A6) and Contemplations (A6).

Our A6 creative activity books contain ideas for a One Day retreat, a Holiday retreat, a Pilgrimage, a Lent and an Advent preparation.

Each book contains prayers and activities split into sections to help you take time out with God.

Please visit our website,

www.lindisfarne-scriptorium.co.uk

to purchase these books and many other items.

Or ask at your local Christian Bookshop as they can order them for you.